GARFIELD

Wassup?

G000243553

JIM DAVIS

℞
RAVETTE PUBLISHING

First published by Ravette Publishing 2011.

Printed in the UK by CPI Cox & Wyman, Reading, RG1 8EX
for Ravette Publishing Limited,
PO Box 876
Horsham
West Sussex RH12 9GH

ISBN: 978-1-84161-355-0

I HAD A BAD HAIRCUT

TWO WRONGS DON'T MAKE A RIGHT, PAL!

JIM DAVIS 11-1

IF SANTA BRINGS ME WHAT I WANT, HE GETS THE HAT BACK

JIM DAVIS 12-5

BOING!

GOT A TRAMPOLINE FOR CHRISTMAS

JIM DAVIS 12-28

SLURP!

SCHLURP

HOW'S YOUR HOT CHOCOLATE?

FINE. AND YOURS?

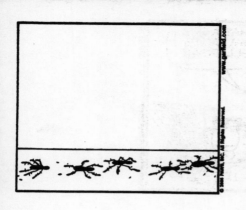

Distributed by Universal Press Syndicate

Distributed by Universal Press Syndicate

JIM DAVIS 2-11

KEEP
OFF
THE
GRASS

JIM DAVIS 3-3

OTHER GARFIELD BOOKS AVAILABLE

Classics (cont'd ...)	**Price**	**ISBN**
Volume Nineteen	£6.99	978-1-84161-303-1
Volume Twenty	£6.99	978-1-84161 304-8
New title available Aug 2011 ...		
Volume Twenty One	£7.99	978-1-84161-359-8
Gift Books		
30 years - the fun's just begun	£9.99	978-1-84161-307-9
Don't Know, Don't Care	£4.99	978-1-84161-279-9
Get a Grip	£4.99	978-1-84161-282-9
I Don't Do Ordinary	£4.99	978-1-84161-281-2
Keep your Attitude, I have my own	£4.99	978-1-84161-278-2
Little Books		
C-c-c-caffeine	£2.50	978-1-84161-183-9
Food 'n' Fitness	£2.50	978-1-84161-145-7
Laughs	£2.50	978-1-84161-146-4
Love 'n' Stuff	£2.50	978-1-84161-147-1
Surf 'n' Sun	£2.50	978-1-84161-186-0
The Office	£2.50	978-1-84161-184-6
Zzzzzz	£2.50	978-1-84161-185-3
Miscellaneous		
Colour Collection Book 3	£11.99	978-1-84161-320-8
Colour Collection Book 2	£10.99	978-1-84161-306-2
Colour Collection Book 1	£10.99	978-1-84161-293-5
Treasury 7	£10.99	978-1-84161-248-5
Treasury 6	£10.99	978-1-84161-229-4
Treasury 5	£10.99	978-1-84161-198-3
Treasury 4	£10.99	978-1-84161-180-8
Treasury 3	£9.99	978-1-84161-142-6
How to Draw Garfield & Friends	£3.99	978-1-84161-334-5
Garfield & Co graphic novel	£6.99	978-1-84161-349-9

All Garfield books are available at your local bookshop or from the publisher at the address below.

Just send your order with your payment and name and address details to:-

Ravette Publishing Ltd
PO Box 876
Horsham
West Sussex RH12 9GH
(tel: 01403 711443 ... email: ingrid@ravettepub.co.uk)

Prices and availability are subject to change without notice.

Please enclose a cheque or postal order made payable to **Ravette Publishing** to the value of the cover price of the book/s and allow the following for UK postage and packing:-

70p for the first book + 40p for each additional book
except Treasuries & Colour Collections... when please add £3.00 per book